Danger! Tricky question ...

Have you ever rescued someone?

This story is based on something that really happened when I was a child. My brother and I saved a friend who got stuck on a raft in a flooded stream. He was heading for a pipe as well. But that pipe went under a road. We only just got him out in time. It was really scary.

For Isabelle and William

It was Saturday morning and Lee and Dan were chilling out in the woods. Suddenly Lee saw an old coin.

He picked it up and flipped it over.

It said **danger** on one side and **dare** on the other.

"What does that mean?" asked Dan.

"Don't know," said Lee, shrugging his shoulders. "It could be a coin from some kid's game."

He tossed it in the air and it made an odd humming sound.

"Look how it's landed," said Dan. "It says **danger**."

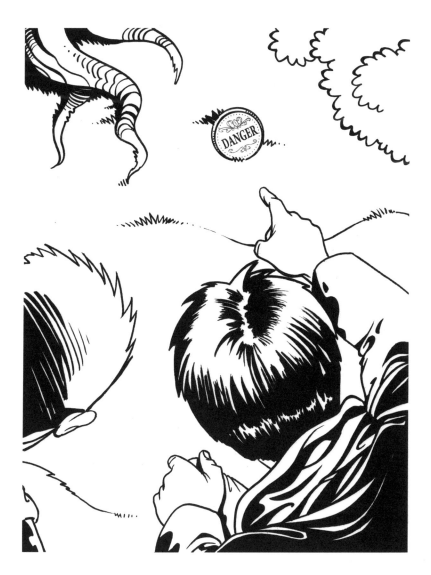

Just then they heard a shout coming
from the far end of the woods. Someone
was yelling for help.

They ran on into the woods till they came to a stream. They saw that it was flooded and the water was very deep.

Then they saw a raft. It was spinning in the water. A kid was holding on to it. He looked very, very scared.

"Help!" he yelled. "I can't hold on much longer."

"I'll see if I can get to him," said Dan, running along the bank. But he saw that the stream vanished down into a big pipe under the ground.

He ran back to Lee.

"The raft will go into that pipe over there," he said. "We must save the kid before he gets sucked into it. But how can we get him?"

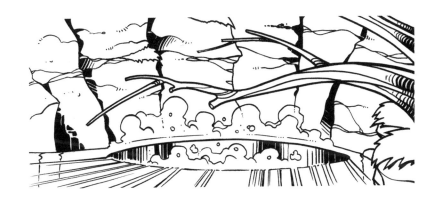

Lee saw a branch hanging over the stream.

It was just before the water went into the pipe.

"Follow me!" he said.

Lee climbed along the branch. Dan was just behind him. The raft was spinning round getting nearer and nearer to the pipe.

"Hold on to me, Dan," said Lee. "Don't
let go!"

The raft shot under the branch. Just
then, Lee grabbed the kid's arms and pulled
him up off the raft.

Seconds later the raft smashed into the pipe and broke into bits.

Dan, Lee and the kid watched as the bits of the raft vanished down the pipe.

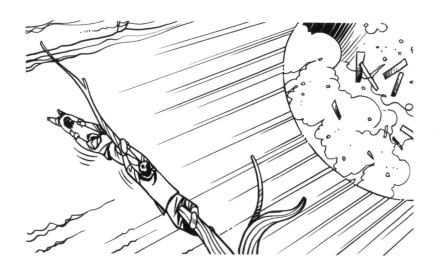

"That was close," said Dan.

"Too close," said Lee.

"That was cool!" said the kid. "I'll make another raft when I get home, then we can do it again!"

Like this book? Why not try the next one?

Ghost

The coin says **Dare**.

Will Dan and Lee go into the old house? And
what will they find inside?

For more info check out our website:
www.barringtonstoke.co.uk

DARE OR DANGER

Watch out for more **Dare or Danger** books coming soon ...

The Cliff

The coin shows Danger.

Can Lee survive his fall from the cliff?

Dare You?

The coin shows Dare.

Will Dan and Lee beat the bully?

For more info check out our website:
www.barringtonstoke.co.uk